SHOPKINS: 2018

A CENTUM BOOK 9781911460893

Published in Great Britain by Centum Books Ltd

This edition published 2017

1 3 5 7 9 10 8 6 4 2

Centum Books Ltd, 20 Devon Square, Newton Abbot, Devon TQ12 2HR, UK

books@centumbooksltd.co.uk

CENTUM BOOKS Limited Reg. No. 07641486

A CIP catalogue record for this book is available from the British Library

Printed in China

# Shopkins™

*Once you shop...You can't stop!*

# 2018
## This SHOPKINS™ book belongs to:

_____

centum

## WHAT'S INSIDE?

# WELCOME TO SHOPVILLE!

Hello Shopkins fans! Are you ready for a super-fun Shopville adventure? This book is packed full of all your old Shopkins favourites from seasons 1–4, as well as baskets full of new friends to meet and greet from seasons 5–8!

Don't forget all the Shoppies, too! There are also a few new Shoppies and their BFFs to hang out with.

With puzzles, games, crafts, quizzes and I LOVE SPK fun, you are going to have an adorable time!

## YOU READY?
## LET'S GO SHOPPING!

## LOVE, FUN,
## LAUGH
### WITH SHOPKINS!

# CAN YOU SPOT?

Inside you are going to make LOTS of new friends!
Hidden along the way are a couple of old favourites, too.
Can you spot these Shopkins? Tick them off as you find them!

 **Strawberry Kiss** ☐     **Sneaky Wedge** ☐     **Chee Zee** ☐

 **Dum Mee Mee** ☐     **Chatter** ☐     **Casper Cap** ☐

# BAGS READY!

It's slumber party time! Help the Shopkins get packed for their super-cool sleepover. Which Shopkins are being packed into Olive Overnight Bag?

SLEEPOVERS WITH MY BESTIES!

OLIVE OVERNIGHT BAG

# MAKE-UP MUDDLE

No slumber party is a party without some make-up Shopkins! Can you find the four make-up Shopkins in this muddle?

ANSWERS ON **PAGE 60**

# WHO AM I?

**The Shopkins are playing Who Am I?**
**Can you guess the Shopkins mystery guest from the clues below?**

**1** I run but never get anywhere!

**2** I have a clean-and-bubbly personality.

**3** My favourite time is just before bedtime!

Use the Shopkins shadow below to help you guess.

# COSY CLOSE-UPS

At the start of every slumber party you've got to get cosy! Can you match the close-ups to the cosy Shopkins below? Which close-up is the odd one out?

**JESSIE DRESSING GOWN**

**1**

**2**

**3**

**4**

**5**

**6**

**ANNA PAJAMAS**

**ROLLY SLEEPING BAG**

**SANDY SHUT EYE**

**BUN BUN SLIPPER**

# PHONE-A-FRIEND PUZZLES

Can you work out who these slumber partygoers' best buddies are?
Decode the word wheels below by crossing out the first letter on each
wheel, then every other letter to discover the answers!

**1** START

**2** START

**3** START

# SLUMBER SHADOWS

Who is having a midnight feast? Can you match these Shopkins shadows to
the correct midnight feasters? Which feaster doesn't have a shadow?

1  a  2  b  3  c

d  4  e  5  f

ANSWERS ON **PAGE 60**

# SLUMBER PHOTO

What a great slumber party! The Shopkins have taken a selfie.
Can you spot which photo is the odd one out? The odd photo out
has five differences – can you find them all?

SLUMBER PARTY

1

SLUMBER PARTY

TIME FOR
A SLEEPOVER
SELFIE!
SPK BFFs!

2

SLUMBER PARTY

3

SLUMBER PARTY

4

SLUMBER PARTY

# MEET SEASON 5

## CREAMY COOKIE CUPCAKE

She's three treats in one... cookies, cream and yummy cupcake!

♥ s having sweet dreams.

## FREDA FERN

She's fern-loving with a growing circle of friends.

♥ s to branch out and try new things.

## ICE CREAM KATE

The coolest partygoer of all, she's always on trend and loves gifts!

♥ s getting the scoop on what's new.

## LOLA ROLLER BLADE

A wheelie-fast scootin' boot, who's a bit of a show-off!

♥ s to rock 'n' roll.

## MEL T MOMENT

She's soft sweetness from top to middle. Watch out! She's made to melt your heart.

♥ s being the soft-centre of attention.

## TAMMY TAMBOURINE

A real shaker and mover who likes to groove to her own beat.

♥ s to shake, rattle and roll.

## BAKERY

## DOLLY DONUT

"Rolly" sweet and "rolly" friendly, she's the perfect friend for a tasty tea party!

♥ s having "rolls" of fun!

## LINDA LAYERED CAKE

She's got layers to her! A slice is three times as yummy and nice.

♥ s to please with layers of loveliness.

## ROYAL CUPCAKE

A treat fit for royalty, but she's always leaving crumbs on the red carpet!

♥ s royal tea parties.

# SWEET TREATS

## CUTE FRUIT JELLO
Can be wobbly on her feet, but she always has a clear head!

♥ s wobbly good birthday parties.

## SPRINKLE LEE CAKE
A super-sweet treat that has hundreds of thousands of things to show her friends.

♥ s a sprinkle of happiness.

# SPORT

## DENNIS BAT
Can be a bit highly strung and tense, but always serves up and delivers when it counts!

♥ s to rally for a good cause.

## KATIE SKATEBOARD
A risk taker who loves tasty tricks, but can flip out when her friends are watching.

♥ s to roll and glide.

## GRACE BASEBALL BAT
Can be a little swing and miss, but is always a hit when it comes to having a ball with her friends.

♥ s to strike it lucky.

## BESSIE BASEBALL
A real high-flyer who is always pitching in to help her friends. Likes a good joke that can leave her in stitches.

♥ s to catch up with friends.

## BAILEY BASEBALL GLOVE
A truly great catch! She is a handy friend who never drops the ball.

♥ s playing catch with friends.

# MEET SEASON 5

## HOMEWARES

### BERTHA BATH
Has a warm and bubbly personality and is good clean fun! Loves to run, but always has time to chill and relax!
♥s a good splash about.

### LYNN LAMP
She's very switched-on and always has lots of bright ideas. Can also be a little light-headed!
♥s a bedtime story.

### TINY TISSUES
Can be eager to please after every sneeze! Will catch her friends' tears or a big nose blow.
♥s being on hand to help tidy up.

### JEN JUG
Can handle any hot situation without flipping her lid. She is always cool-headed when things start to heat up.
♥s going out for drinks with her friends.

### POLLY TEAPOT
She's prim and proper, especially with it's time for tea! Life is never boring when she is pouring.
♥s time for tea.

## GARDEN

## TECH

### PENNY WISHING WELL
A lucky friend to know, she always offers her best wishes to everyone!
♥s feeling happy and well.

### WOODY GARDEN CHAIR
Likes to sit around outside and listen to birdsong. A great friend to know after a long, busy day.
♥s to sit and relax.

### CONNIE CONSOLE
She has quite a controlling personality, so don't push her buttons because she might lose it!
♥s being hands-on and in control.

# MUSIC

## POLLY PIANO

The key to her happiness is being in tune with her emotions and her best friends.

♥s to play 24/7.

## HILLARY HARP

Has the heart of an angel! She always puts her friends to sleep with her dreamy music.

♥s to sing like an angel.

## LIMITED EDITION

## PAULA PUZZLE

Organised and loves everything in the right place. Can get a little puzzled when her world tips upside-down.

♥s solving stuff!

## LYNNE SPRING

Always has a spring in her step! Can be a bit clumsy and will fall down stairs easily!

♥s spring cleaning.

## YOLANDA YO-YO

Highly strung, but loves winding up her friends. Her life is full of ups and downs.

♥s walking the dog!

## SPINDERELLA

She's always in a spin and a little dizzy. Struggles to go in a straight line, but is good at taking turns.

♥s playing "top" scotch.

## FORTUNE STELLA

Has an answer for everything and can be a bit of a know-it-all!

♥s playing pool.

## BLOCKY

A small but important friend who likes to connect with his besties. Always building new friendships.

♥s "buddy" building.

# SLEEPOVER DREAM-CATCHER

**Here's a fun and crafty activity you can do at home
when you invite your BFFs over for a slumber party!**

## YOU WILL NEED:

- Embroidery hoop
- Colourful tape
- 3 colourful balls of wool
- Felt
- Fabric glue
- Scissors
- Needle and thread

**1**

First use the colourful tape to decorate
the embroidery hoop. You can use
lots of fun patterned sticky tapes, too.
Be creative with your pattern.

**2**

Choose two or three different coloured
wools. Tie the first wool thread to the top
of your embroidery hoop, then tightly loop
and loop around your hoop to create
a fun dream-catcher web.

**3**

Repeat step 2 with the other
coloured wool you have chosen.

**4**

Once your dream-catcher web is
complete, you can start with the hanging
decorations. Choose the coloured felt
you want and cut out a heart shape.

**5**

Now cut a slightly smaller heart shape and use the fabric glue to stick the two heart shapes together.

**6**

When dry, use the needle and thread to attach the hanging heart to your dream-catcher web.

**7**

Now, repeat steps 5 and 6 with other shapes of your choice. You may want to try a star, or an animal shape, such as an owl?

*zzz*
# Five more minutes please

**8**

When all your hanging decorations are complete and attached to the dream-catcher web, your dream-catcher is ready to hang above your bed! Use some wool to create a loop around the top of the hoop, then hang or attach to your wall!

# SLEEPOVER SEARCH

The Shopkins have made lots of new friendship groups.
Can you find each group in the picture search?

ANSWERS ON PAGE 60

**1**

**2**

**3**

**4**

**5**

**6**

# SLEEPOVER GAMES

Here are two super-sweet sleepover games you can
play with your friends at your very own Slumber Party.

## WHICH SHOPKINS?

*This fun guess-the-Shopkins game can be played
with your own Shopkins collection!*

Place all your Shopkins in a pillowcase and one-by-one each player picks a
Shopkins without looking at it. Each player must place their pillow in front of
them and the Shopkins character on the floor in front of the pillow, so they
can't see their own Shopkins character, but everyone else can. Now, players
take it in turns to ask yes-and-no questions to see if they can guess which
Shopkins character they've picked. When a player gets a "no" the
question-asking passes to the player on their left. Play continues in a clockwise
direction, until a player correctly guesses all their Shopkins characters!

## SLUMBER STORIES

*This game is for people who like to tell stories.*

Choose a storyteller, then everyone picks an item in the room.
It can be a Shopkins character, a brush, mirror, smartphone, whatever is
around. Place all the items in a pillowcase and give it to the storyteller.
The storyteller must start their story with the sentence below, then pick
out an item. They then need to include the item in their story. They then
pick another item, and so on until they have included all the items from
the pillowcase in their story. The honour of being storyteller then moves
to the player on the left and the Slumber Stories game starts again.

SPK BFF
Sleepover

"It was getting late and the Slumber Party Shopkins decided to..."

# SHOPPIES COLOUR 'N' COOK

Donatina and Bubbleisha are getting ready to
make 'n' bake in the Chef Club kitchen!

COPY THE PICTURES OF THE SHOPPIES BELOW AND COLOUR THEM IN READY TO COOK!

# SECRET DINNER GUEST

**Donatina and Bubbleisha have invited a special guest to their Chef Club dinner party. Can you find the code and discover who the secret guest is?**

BETWEEN PAGES 22 TO 33 YOU WILL FIND NINE SPECIAL CHEF HATS. INSIDE THE HATS ARE CODE LETTERS. FIND THE CODE LETTERS AND THEN PLACE THEM IN THE CORRECT PLACE ON THE ANSWER GRID BELOW. EACH HAT HAS A NUMBER ON IT, SO YOU KNOW WHERE TO PLACE IT IN THE ANSWER GRID.

Once you have ALL the code letters, use the **CODEBREAKER** grid below to discover the secret dinner guest's name!

| 1 | 2 | 3 | 4 | 5 | 6 | 7 | 8 | 9 |
|---|---|---|---|---|---|---|---|---|
|   |   |   |   |   |   |   |   |   |
|   |   |   |   |   |   |   |   |   |

## CODE

CODE LETTERS →

| G | H | I | J | K | L | M | N | O | P | Q | R | S |
|---|---|---|---|---|---|---|---|---|---|---|---|---|
| A | B | C | D | E | F | G | H | I | J | K | L | M |

CODE LETTERS →

| T | U | V | W | X | Y | Z | A | B | C | D | G | E |
|---|---|---|---|---|---|---|---|---|---|---|---|---|
| N | O | P | Q | R | S | T | U | V | W | X | Y | Z |

# KITCHEN TIDY-UP!

Help the Shopkins tidy up the
Chef Club kitchen with this fun game.

YOU WILL NEED:
2-4 PLAYERS,
A DICE, 4 IDENTICAL
COINS PER PLAYER

FINISH
GREEN
CUPBOARD

SHORTCUT!
TAKE YOUR
PIECE STRAIGHT
TO YOUR
CUPBOARD!

GREEN FINISH
THIS WAY!

ROLL
AGAIN!

BLUE
START

MISS A
TURN!

RED
START

ROLL
AGAIN!

YELLOW FINISH
THIS WAY!

FINISH
YELLOW
CUPBOARD

GO FORWARD
2 SPACES!

22

# HOW TO PLAY

- Each player needs **four identical coins** to use as counters.
- Each player then **chooses a colour** and places their four coins on that colour's Start square.
- The **youngest** player goes first.
- **Roll the dice** and move the number of spaces shown on the dice.
- **The aim of the game** is to get all your coins from your Start square to your colour's cupboard Finish square.
- Coins can only be moved to the cupboard **one at a time**.
- If you land on an **instruction square**, read it out and follow the actions.
- The **winner** is the first player to get all their coins to their Finish square.

GO FORWARD 2 SPACES!

FINISH RED CUPBOARD

RED FINISH THIS WAY!

YELLOW START

ROLL AGAIN!

MISS A TURN!

FLOUR +  =

GREEN START

ROLL AGAIN!

BLUE FINISH THIS WAY!

SHORTCUT! TAKE YOUR PIECE STRAIGHT TO YOUR CUPBOARD!

MISS A TURN!

FINISH BLUE CUPBOARD

# MEET SEASON 6

## CUPCAKE PRINCESS

A treat fit for a princess!
She rules the kitchen with sweetness
and lets everyone eat cake!

♥ s being the sweetest cupcake, ever!

## BUNCHO BANANAS

She is a bunch of fun to hang around with.
Will peel over backwards to help you out.

♥ s eating "bunch" with friends.

## FLEUR FLOUR

Always rises to the occasion and takes the
cake when it comes to makin' and baking!

♥ s to shake things up.

## MISS SPRINKLES

She likes to sprinkle sweetness wherever
she goes! Always looking for something to
decorate in hundreds of thousands of ways!

♥ s showering her friends in colour!

## BERRY TUBS

She's "berry" sweet, "berry" nice and
always "berry" friendly. She's a tub of
fruit that is extra cute!

♥ s quiet nights in with a spoon!

## CHERRY-ANNE

She's a "cherry" special friend, who
is always at the top when you are
looking for a finishing touch.

♥ s being the "stalk" of the town.

## HARVEY HONEYCOMB

He's the bees-knees and when
it comes to the crunch, he's the
number-one sweet choice!

♥ s bee-ing fun!

## CHOC N' CHIP

A pair of crumbly cuties. When one cookie
is never enough, these guys are the
perfect friends to spend time with!

♥ s chasing each other around the plate!

## CASSIE CASTER SUGAR

The perfect problem solver, she
always looks fine and will fix any
sweet disaster!

♥ s sweet times.

## CINNAMON SALLY

Adds a little spice that tastes so nice.
She makes baking taste a "roll" lot
better with one little shake!

♥ s all things nice and spice.

## DUSTY COCOA

A sweet organiser, she is all over it!
Likes to add a finishing touch, but
never too much.

♥ s to add a little chocolatey colour.

## STAPLE

### BETSY BUTTER

Always there to help out in a sticky situation. Her friends melt her heart!

♥s to spread herself about.

### KANE SUGAR

A spoonful of sweetness, she is full of sprinkly good fun and loves to sweet-treat her friends.

♥s to sprinkle sweetness.

### MELISSA MILK

Can be a little emotional and tends to pour her heart out to others.

♥s to chill out and be cool.

### OLIVE OIL

A real morning person, she loves to wake up "oily" and slip out for breakfast with friends.

♥s a big squeeze.

### RUNNY HONEY

Made by bees and is eager to please! A sweet-by-nature friend who will always run to your aid.

♥s knowing the buzz.

### SAM SOY

Full of flavour, this little bottle loves to bring some exotic fun to the table.

♥s travelling the Far East.

### SHELLY EGG

A real softy who loves to help bring friends together. Never likes being separated from the gang!

♥s to crack a joke or two!

### V. NILLA TUBS

She can seem a little cold at the start, but after a while she'll soften and warm up to you!

♥s to keep her cool.

### VICKI VANILLA

A little bottle of big flavour! She can be intense and sometimes she can be a little too much.

♥s to add a splash of flavour to the party.

### KAREN CARROT

Her friends think she is more orange than an orange! But she doesn't "carrot" at all.

♥s to dig in and help out.

### CHOC CHIPS

She's a little bowl of sweet bliss who likes to chip in with sweet ideas.

♥s to sweeten the pot.

### CHOC E. TUBS

Always chilling with his besties and is every chocolate lover's dream date!

♥s to melt in a hot tub!

### WILBUR WHIPPED CREAM

With one touch he can whip up a creamy dream. He has a topping you shouldn't be stopping!

♥s cream-pie fights!

## FAMILY FOOD

### BETHANY BROCCOLI

She's little and green and loves to dream! She's full of goodness and always sprouts a good idea or two.

♥ s eating her greens.

### C. SALT

Likes to be included in everything, savoury or sweet, and doesn't like being left out of the gang.

♥ s going to the C-side!

### CHILI PEPPA

A little pepper who packs a punch! Spicy and hot she likes to add some fun to the pot!

♥ s hot-rod racing!

### JASMINE RICE

One of the nicest rices you will meet! She's very creative and is always having "grainwaves"!

♥ s rice skating.

### NINA NOODLES

Your friend for a very long, long time. She's oodles of fun for everyone!

♥ s rope climbing.

### PAPPA PIZZA BASE

He's always flat out in the kitchen, but always manages to hold it together, even when hot!

♥ s watching base-ball.

### PARMESAN PETE

A bit of a risk taker, who likes a close shave or two, especially when above a bowl of spaghetti!

♥ s a cheesy joke!

### PATSY PASTA

Can be hard-headed to start, but warms up and everyone loves to mix with her!

♥ s making pasta art.

### ROMA TOMATO

A little Italian sweetie who can be a little saucy. Loves to mix with her bestie, Patsy Pasta.

♥ s a Roma holiday!

### TEARY ONION

She's emotional and is always a layer or two away from bursting into tears!

♥ s watching tear-jerkers!

### TIMMY TOMATO PASTE

She's little and green and loves to dream! She's full of goodness and always sprouts a good idea or two.

♥ s eating her greens.

# BREAKFAST

## CHARLIE CHEESE

Likes to be on top of things, but can get a bit melty when things heat up!

♥ s to go with the flow.

## HERB L. TEABAG

A real nature lover who loves nothing more than a hot soak!

♥ s taking a dunk in hot springs.

## MAVIS MAPLE SYRUP

A real sweet friend who sticks by you – thick or thin! You can never get enough of her on your plate!

♥ s sticky situations.

## PIPPA LEMON

If life gives you lemons, ask for Pippa! She's not bitter and will become your new, zesty bestie!

♥ s making lemonade!

## ROS BERRY

A shy little berry who gets embarrassed easily and will blush as red as a raspberry.

♥ s the "berry" holidays.

## SMALL-FRY PAN

A little pan that can handle a lot of heat. But don't mention pancakes or she will flip-out!

♥ s to "fry" and do her best.

## SUSIE SAUSAGE

A bit of a high "fryer", she is a colourful character who likes to change with the times.

♥ s dressing to "grill".

## TOAST T. WARM

Warm, friendly and is always at the bottom of everything at breakfast time.

♥ s to toast his friends.

## LIMITED EDITION

## BELINDA BLENDER

Always in a spin, she loves whirling around the dancefloor with her favourite ingredients!

♥ s a ballroom blitz!

## BESSIE BOWL

She loves to dance and has a secret ambition stirring inside her - she wants to be a "Bowlywood" star!

♥ s going bowl-ing!

## JUDY JUG

Always measures up to others' expectations! Can handle anything, but her emotions can overflow.

♥ s juggling!

## PATRICIA PARFAIT GLASS

She's in a "glass" of her own and can make the perfect parfait for every party!

♥ s dessert island dreaming!

## PATTY CASE

Can always hold her own with the best of them and always feels fulfilled. You "batter" believe it!

♥ s baking, baking and… baking!

## PIZZA WILL

Is a real Mr. Slice Guy who loves to cut to the chase! He's also a "wheel" sharp dresser!

♥ s unicycling!

## TINY TIARA TOPPER

A royal tiara who is barely seen, but she still makes every dish feel like a queen!

♥ s playing dress-up!

## WHITNEY WHISK

She can mix it up with the best of them, but never stirs up any trouble!

♥ s beating the lumps!

# CHEF CLUB QUIZ

What type of Chef Clubber are YOU? Are you a super starter,
or a magnificent main, or maybe you're a delicious dessert?
Answer the questions below to find out!

**1** You are out with friends and want a snack. Do you...

a Order something quick and small, there's more shopping to do!
b Go for a nice tasty meal, so you can have a sit down and gossip.
c Head to the ice-cream parlour! Three scoops for you!

**2** You grab some toast before heading off for a morning meet-up with besties. Do you...

a Just grab half a slice of buttered toast.
b Decide to stop and cook-up some eggs and mushrooms to go with it.
c Thickly spread on some yummy jam and enjoy!

**3** It's movie night with friends. What movie do you choose to watch?

a The Breakfast Club
b Cloudy With a Chance of Meatballs
c Chocolat

**4** For a day shopping with your BFFs, do you...

a Dress causal and quick. Time to shop!
b Go for something practical - it's gotta last all day!
c Pop on something sweet, bubbly and cute!

**5** After a busy day shopping, gossiping and hanging out. Do you...

a Grab something quick and easy from the fridge when you get home.
b Carry on the fun and go for a dinner out with your mates.
c Head to the café and gossip some more over cupcakes and donuts.

## MOSTLY As:
### SUPER STARTER
For you something small,
tasty and easy is the
perfect foodie treat.

## MOSTLY Bs:
### MAGNIFICENT MAIN
For you it's all about the
main event. You're a sucker
for a savoury feast!

## MOSTLY Cs:
### DELICIOUS DESSERT
It's all about your sweet tooth!
You're at your best with a
d'lish tasty treat to eat!

28

ANSWERS ON PAGE 60

# TIDY KITCHEN

What a messy kitchen! Can you match and tidy the Shopkins into groups, so you can get started on another super-sweet bake?

**FRUIT SHOPKINS**

1. _____
2. _____
3. _____

**BAKING SHOPKINS**

1. _____
2. _____
3. _____

**UTENSILS SHOPKINS:**

1. _____
2. _____
3. _____

# MISSING INGREDIENT

Are you ready to start another bake? First, let's check we have all the ingredients. The list below has everything you need. Check pages 32–33 and look for each Shopkins then tick them off the list. The Shopkins who isn't on either page is the missing ingredient!

## SHOPKINS LIST

- ☐ PIPPA LEMON
- ☐ CHERRY-ANNE
- ☐ BUNCHO BANANAS
- ☐ WHITNEY WHISK
- ☐ JUDY JUG
- ☐ BESSIE BOWL
- ☐ SHELLY EGG
- ☐ FLEUR FLOUR

- ☐ MISS SPRINKLES
- ☐ RUNNY HONEY
- ☐ VICKI VANILLA
- ☐ CHOC CHIPS
- ☐ MELISSA MILK
- ☐ BELINDA BLENDER
- ☐ BERRY TUBS
- ☐ MELONIE PIPS

- ☐ POSH PEAR
- ☐ PINEAPPLE CRUSH
- ☐ STRAWBERRY KISS
- ☐ JUICY ORANGE
- ☐ KANE SUGAR
- ☐ BETSY BUTTER

# ROYAL PARTY CAKES

Cupcake Princess is planning a tea party.
Can you design some scrumptious cupcakes for the royal event?

**COLOUR AND DECORATE THEM WITH YOUR FAVOURITE FLAVOURS!**

# TABLECLOTH TRAVELS

The Chef Club Shopkins are playing a fun number maze game! Can you
help Runny Honey find her way to her zesty bestie, Pippa Lemon?
Runny Honey can only step on even numbers.

| START | 2 | 8 | 11 | 12 | 20 | 6 | 22 | 1 | 9 |
|-------|----|----|----|----|----|----|----|----|----|
| 13 | 5 | 12 | 15 | 4 | 7 | 21 | 14 | 3 | 47 |
| 5 | 11 | 4 | 13 | 46 | 37 | 49 | 10 | 51 | 9 |
| 3 | 17 | 22 | 18 | 6 | 53 | 23 | 6 | 36 | 41 |
| 31 | 19 | 37 | 1 | 45 | 17 | 35 | 57 | 26 | 20 FINISH |

ANSWERS ON PAGE 60

# MAIN COURSE CLUES

What is the Chef Club cooking up now? Follow the clues below to see if you can work out what tasty treat is being whipped up in the kitchen.

**1** The dish doesn't have any feet.

**2** The dish has green eyes.

**3** The dish has both eyes open.

**TWIRLY SPAGHETTI**

**SAMI SCRAMBLES**

**STACKS COOKIE**

**B.NANA SPLIT**

# COOKIE DRAW

Can you finish off this tasty picture of scrumptious Stacks Cookie?
There is a guide to help you out!

**NOW COLOUR STACKS COOKIE IN!**

# MEET THE SHOPPIES!

The Shoppies love to shop, hang out, chat and shop some more! Come and meet the squad!

I love getting stuck into shopping, but sometimes it can get me into a few sticky situations!

♥s Relaxing in a bubble-gum bubble bath!

BFFs: Bubblicious and Bubble Cupcake

## BUBBLEISHA

I'm a little sweetie at heart and I love to pop out and spend the day shopping with my besties.

♥s Decorating cupcakes!

BFFs: Cherry Nice Cupcake and Cupcake Petal

## JESSICAKE

It looks like I'm always chilled, but I also have a warm heart! If you have any gossip, I'd love to get the latest scoop!

♥s Chilling out with my BFFs!

BFFs: Choc Mint Charlie and Nice Cream Sandwich

## PEPPA-MINT

I love having a "hole" lot of fun and I'm always "round" to spend time with my sweet BFFs!

♥s Hanging out at my donut cart!

BFFs: Dippy Donut and Chrissy Cream

## DONATINA

I love being bright and colourful in everything I do, wear and eat! I love to cheer up my friends with a bit of rainbow therapy!

♥s Painting the town in rainbows!

BFFs: Rayne-Bow and Raylene Rainbow

## RAINBOW KATE

I love having all the hot new colours and styles at my fingertips! It's all about the complete look - from head to fingernail!

♥s Filing my nails.

BFFs: Natalie Nail Polish and Bessie Brush

## POLLI POLISH

I love being "pout" and about with my besties! I'm bright, glossy and a little bossy!

♥s Giving makeovers.
BFFs: Marcee Makeup Bag and Iris Eye Shadow

## LIPPY LULU

I'm really down to earth and I love showering my besties with blooming wonderful gifts!

♥s Making beautiful bouquets.
BFFs: Whitney Watering Can and Maisy Daisy

## DAISY PETALS

I'm a little soft-centred and a real sweetheart! I'm always chasing chocolate and have a head full of sweet dreams!

♥s Eating chocolate!
BFFs: Hayley Sweet Heart and Roxy Chock Block

## COCOLETTE

I'm all about grace and style! I love to dress to impress – nothing is "tutu" cute! Every day is a show, so practise makes perfect!

♥s Performing good turns for my friends.
BFFs: Tutu and Tippy and Toes

## PIROUETTA

I'm a little sweet and cheeky, but can sometimes get stuck in a fruity mix! I love to delight my friends with a scrummy summertime treat!

♥s Mixing with my friends!
BFFs: Ruthie Smoothie and Pamela Parfait

## LUCY SMOOTHIE

I'm a prim and proper shopper and love to end the day with a hot cuppa! No sugar for me – I'm sweet enough already!

♥s Hosting super-sweet tea parties.
BFFs: Tessa Teacup and Sugar E. Bowl

## KIRSTEA

# PUZZLES

# INVITATION MISPRINT!

Rainbow Bite is organising a Rainbow Celebration Party! But all her invitations have printed wrong! Don't worry, one invite is correct. Can you find it? It is the one that is different to all the others.

**1**   **2**   **3**

**4**   **5**   **6**

# CELEBRATE CREATE!

The Shopkins are super-excited about the Rainbow Celebration Party! Can you copy this picture of an excited Party Plate who has just received her invitation?

FINISHED?
NOW, COLOUR IT IN!

USE THE GRID SQUARES TO HELP YOU DRAW!

ANSWERS ON PAGE 60-61

# PERFECT BUNTING!

**Rainbow Bite and D'lish Donut have gone bunting shopping for the party! Work out which bunting Rainbow Bite thinks is super-sweet by following the clues below.**

**1** THE BUNTING HAS SEVEN FLAGS ON IT.

**2** IT HAS A PINK FLAG.

**3** THERE IS ONLY ONE RED FLAG.

**4** THE ORANGE FLAG IS NEXT TO THE RED FLAG.

# GUEST LIST SEARCH

**Strawberry Kiss and Miss Sprinkles have a list of people they need to invite to the Rainbow Celebration Party. Can you find the characters in the Shopkins grid?**

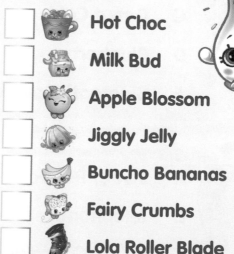

- Hot Choc
- Milk Bud
- Apple Blossom
- Jiggly Jelly
- Buncho Bananas
- Fairy Crumbs
- Lola Roller Blade
- Bessy Baseball

# SHOPKINS CREATOR

There's a special place at the party for a BRAND-NEW Shopkins.
Do you want to create your own Shopkins bestie to go with you?
Follow the instructions below to invent your own Shopkins character!

TO CREATE YOUR OWN SHOPKINS BFF YOU NEED TO COLLECT 2 SHOPKINS TOKENS BY ANSWERING THE QUESTIONS BELOW. THEN TAKE THE TOKENS TO THE SPECIAL SHOPKINS-A-MAKER MACHINE.

## TOKEN QUESTION 1

### WHAT'S YOUR FAVOURITE COLOUR?

| | |
|---|---|
| BLUE... | YOUR FIRST TOKEN IS NUMBER 1! |
| YELLOW... | YOUR FIRST TOKEN IS NUMBER 2! |
| RED... | YOUR FIRST TOKEN IS NUMBER 3! |
| GREEN... | YOUR FIRST TOKEN IS NUMBER 4! |
| ORANGE... | YOUR FIRST TOKEN IS NUMBER 5! |
| PURPLE... | YOUR FIRST TOKEN IS NUMBER 6! |
| PINK... | YOUR FIRST TOKEN IS NUMBER 7! |
| BROWN... | YOUR FIRST TOKEN IS NUMBER 8! |
| BLACK OR WHITE... | YOUR FIRST TOKEN IS NUMBER 9! |
| ALL OF THE ABOVE!... | YOUR FIRST TOKEN IS NUMBER 10! |

## TOKEN QUESTION 2

### ARE YOU...

| | |
|---|---|
| SIMPLE AND SAFE?... | YOUR SECOND TOKEN IS A! |
| PRACTICAL AND USEFUL?... | YOUR SECOND TOKEN IS B! |
| SWEET AND DELICIOUS?... | YOUR SECOND TOKEN IS C! |
| NATURAL AND HEALTHY?... | YOUR SECOND TOKEN IS D! |
| HI-TECH AND HANDY?... | YOUR SECOND TOKEN IS E! |

GOT YOUR TOKENS? Now find the compartment that matches your number token.
Inside you'll find an item that matches your letter token!

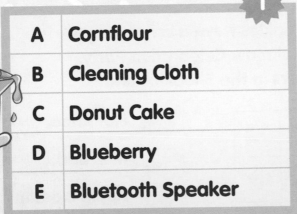

### 1

| | |
|---|---|
| A | Cornflour |
| B | Cleaning Cloth |
| C | Donut Cake |
| D | Blueberry |
| E | Bluetooth Speaker |

### 2

| | |
|---|---|
| A | Cheese |
| B | Cleaning Spray |
| C | Lemon Pie |
| D | Banana |
| E | Sun Lamp |

### 3

| | |
|---|---|
| A | Sweet Pepper |
| B | Telephone |
| C | Velvet Cupcake |
| D | Tomato |
| E | Virtual Reality Goggles |

### 4

| | |
|---|---|
| A | Canned Peas |
| B | Plastic Plant |
| C | Apple Donut |
| D | Lime |
| E | Solar Panel |

| 5 | |
|---|---|
| A | Baked Beans |
| B | Sweetie Candle |
| C | Apricot Yoghurt |
| D | Carrot |
| E | Smartphone |

| 6 | |
|---|---|
| A | Pickled Beetroot |
| B | Cushion |
| C | Raspberry Jam |
| D | Red Cabbage |
| E | Tablet |

| 7 | |
|---|---|
| A | Pork Pie |
| B | Feather Duster |
| C | Candy Crunch |
| D | Radish |
| E | Secret Safe |

| 8 | |
|---|---|
| A | Crusty Bread |
| B | Bookcase |
| C | Chocolate Cake |
| D | Potato |
| E | Computer |

| 9 | |
|---|---|
| A | Salt and Pepper |
| B | Chalkboard |
| C | Dark Choc |
| D | Spring Onion |
| E | Electric Piano |

| 10 | |
|---|---|
| A | Breakfast Treat |
| B | Disco Ball |
| C | Sweetie Cake |
| D | Organic Basket |
| E | Fairy Lights |

Now you have your item, can you think of a fun FIRST NAME?
IT COULD BE YOUR OWN NAME OR SOMETHING AS SUPER-SWEET!

## MY SHOPKINS BFF's NAME IS:

WHY NOT TRY THE SHOPKINS-A-MAKER MACHINE WITH A FRIEND?

# MEET SEASON 7

## DISCO PARTY

### GROOVY GLASSES

Loves it when everyone's eyes are on her
when she's on the dancefloor!

♥s playing "I Spy".

### MIA MIRROR BALL

She is always in a spin and shines on the dancefloor
as soon as the light switch is flicked on!

♥s disco dancing.

### NIKKI MIXIE DESK

Gets the party started every time! She
has so many tracks in her head she has
tunes coming out of her ears!

♥s mixing and matching outfits.

### SQUEEKY SPEAKER

A little speaker who packs a big punch!
Can be pretty noisy at bedtime and
keeps everyone awake!

♥s boom boxing.

## FANCY DRESS PARTY

### FIONA FAIRY SKIRT

When she gets together with Phoebe Fairy Top they
become the most magical looking couple in Shopville.

♥s picking flowers to wear.

### PHOEBE FAIRY TOP

When she's about all you have to do is
imagine and your dreams can come true!

♥s pottering about in her fairy garden.

### SKIP & FLIP FAIRY SLIPPERS

When they get together and tap their heels three times
they make magic! "There's no place like Shopville!"

♥s reading fairy tales.

### WITCHY HAT

Loves performing tricks, but really
she's a treat to be around!

♥s practising her spell-ings!

# PICNIC PARTY

## CREAMY BISCUIT

Loves to greet her friends with a rosy smile! She's pretty from top to bottom and always has good taste!

♥ s sharing afternoon tea.

## MALLORY WATERMELON PUNCH

Super popular on a hot summer's day. It's refreshing to meet someone with a naturally sweet personality.

♥ s dancing in "splash mobs".

## BITZY BISCUIT

Tiny, sweet and petite, she scares easily and tends to crumble at the first sign of any danger!

♥ s tea dunking!

## TINY TEACUP

A cute little cup who is always seen with her biscuit buddies. They all love playing the game "Dunk for Cookies"!

♥ s having tea parties!

# PJ PARTY

## ANNA PAJAMAS

A bit of a night owl. Likes to stay in and rarely goes outside the house.

♥ s watching late-night TV!

## FIZZY SODA

A bubbly personality, but she can sometimes get up her friends' noses.

♥ s fizz-ical activity!

## FLUFFY SLIPPER

Warm-hearted and very loyal, when she says she will do something she never gets "cold feet"!

♥ s cold night walks in the park!

# PRINCESS PARTY

## DIANA DRESS

Always on the best-dressed list, she loves to dress for every occasion, especially princess parties!

♥ s day spas at the Laundromat.

## PRINCESS PURSE

Looks richer than she actually is! She doesn't need to show the dough to make friends, she's already priceless!

♥ s having a royal ball!

## PRINCESS SCENT

A big-hearted friend with a majestic bouquet. Always truthful, she likes to "spray" it like it is!

♥ s smelling like roses!

## SHOES ROYALE

A pretty pair who are true sole-mates! Nobody can trick this couple, they are always on their toes!

♥ s tap dance lessons!

# MEET SEASON 7

### POLLY POOL RING
A playful ring who's a little wet behind the ears, but likes to be "round" when you need her!

♥ s surf life saving.

### SCARLETTE SCOOPS
Can be a little cold until she warms to you. Then you discover how sweet she really is!

♥ s spoon skiing!

### SPLASHY BEACH BALL
A bouncy kind of guy who's a dreamer and a loveable air-head! His biggest fears are needles and being washed out to sea!

♥ s beach volleyball!

### SUE SUNDAE
An absolute treat to meet! Full of fun and sometimes goes over the top!

♥ s visiting "sundae" markets.

### WAFER TOPS
When it comes to being cool, she's the tops! She always has the scoop on the gossip in Shopville!

♥ s ice skating.

## SURPRISE PARTY

### GIGI GIFT
She's always wrapped to be invited to any party and is such a giving friend.

♥ s playing guessing games.

### GRACIE BIRTHDAY CAKE
Thinks life is always sweet! She likes sharing what she has with others!

♥ s singing happy birthday!

### LIL' BLAZE
Can be a little hot-headed! Sometimes a bit hard of hearing because she gets a lot of wax in her ears!

♥ s toasting marshmallows.

### SPARKY & FLICKER
Two wishful thinkers who hate windy days. Always the light of the party!

♥ s granting wishes.

## BETTY BOUQUET

Some say she was "scent" from up above
to brighten this special day of love.

♥s flower pressing.

## LIL' BLISS RING

Is a true romantic. She loves holding bands with
her friends and her name has a lovely ring to it!

♥s doing her nails.

## LIL' WEDDING DRESS

A real beauty who always looks like a
princess. So pretty she brings tears to her
friends' eyes when they first see her!

♥s looking at her wedding album.

## WONDA WEDDING CAKE

A cut above the rest when it comes to beautiful cakes.
She likes to share her love around on the big day!

♥s watching "The Bachelor".

# HOLLYWOOD LIMITED EDITION

## SOPHIE TROPHIE

A bit of an attention seeker
who's always invited to the most
glamorous Hollywood parties.

♥s writing acceptance speeches.

## STARLET MOVIE CAMERA

Loves to be close-up to her friends.
She's very down to earth because
she likes to keep it "reel"!

♥s making home movies.

## PARIS PURSE

A true A-lister who's always seen on
the red carpet. So beautiful she steals
the scene no matter who she's with!

♥s shopping at boutiques.

## STILETTO STELLA

Loves to step out on the dance floor at all the
Hollywood parties. She's living the high life.

♥s shoe shopping for friends.

## KIMMY CAMERA

Super-fast and funny, she's always there in a
flash with a great big smile. Has a photographic
memory and is always taking selfies!

♥s photography, of course!

## ANNE ACTION

Always ready for action, she is an
amazing actor and only needs one
take to wrap up the scene.

♥s watching action movies.

# GROOVY SHADOWS

The lights are low at the party and the Shopkins are moving and grooving. Can you match the Shopkins to their shadows on the dance floor?

# PARTY PATTERNS

The Rainbow Celebration Party is in full swing and everyone is having a colourful time! Can you count how many of each Shopkins is in the party pattern?

 HOT CHOC ☐     JIGGLY JELLY ☐    MEL T. MOMENT ☐

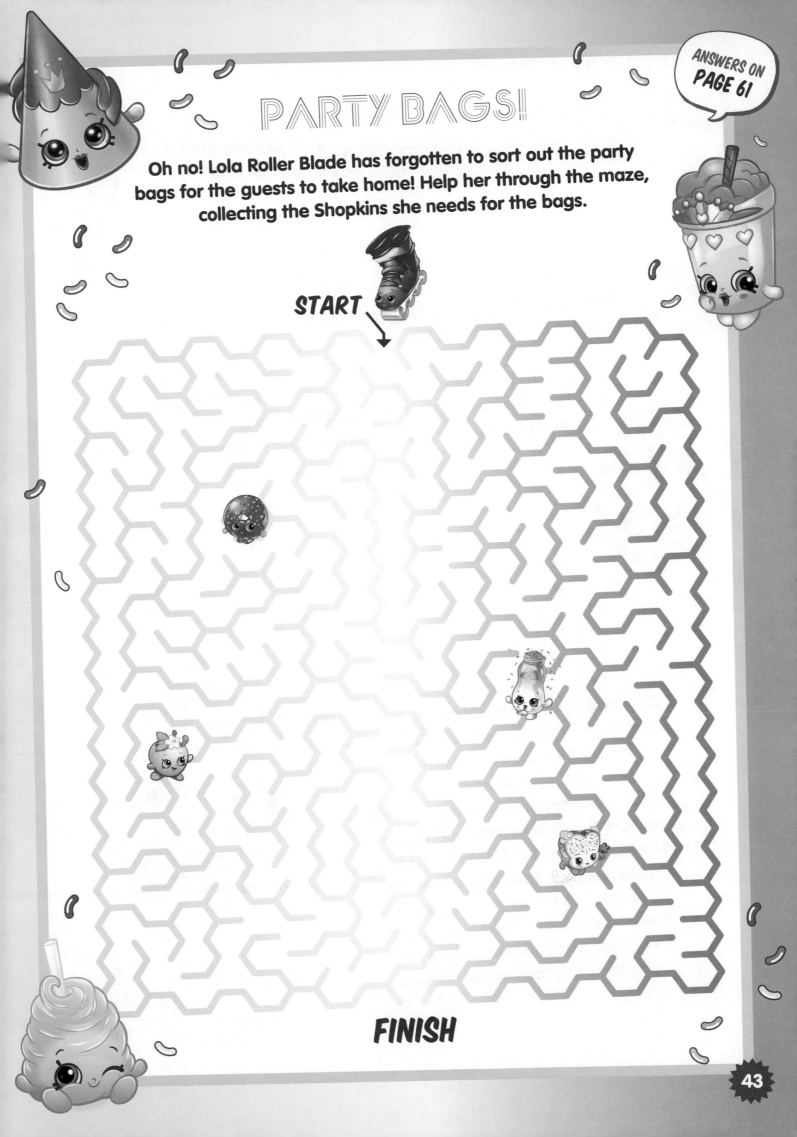

# PARTY BAGS!

Oh no! Lola Roller Blade has forgotten to sort out the party bags for the guests to take home! Help her through the maze, collecting the Shopkins she needs for the bags.

ANSWERS ON PAGE 61

START

FINISH

# PARTY GAMES TO PLAY

**Are you thinking about organising a party? Here are two fun party games you could play at your big bash!**

## WHO'S THE MYSTERY GUEST

This is a fun clues activity for guests to play. First choose a Shopkins character from your collection and find a cool hiding place at the party. NOW, COMES THE CREATIVE BIT. You'll need five envelopes and five "clue cards". Write five clues that will lead the partygoers from clue to clue, and finally to the hidden Shopkins! You can make the clues as easy or as tricky as you like.

### HAVE FUN AND GET YOUR THINKING HAT ON!

## SHOPKINS CHARADES!

**This classic game has a Shopkins twist! Instead of trying to "act-out" books, films and TV shows, you have to "act-out" a Shopkins character! Place your Shopkins collection in a hat or bag, then the "acting-out" player secretly picks a Shopkins from the hat. The player must then only use actions to describe to the other players which Shopkins character he/she has picked. The player who guesses correctly then becomes the "acting-out" player.**

POLISH UP ON YOUR ACTING SKILLS! TO PLAY OR NOT TO PLAY?

ANSWERS ON **PAGE 61**

# DANCE QUEEN

The dance-off is now over and the the judges have decided who the queen of the dance floor will be...

CAN YOU WORK OUT WHO WON?

?

## CLUES

SYLLABLE **1** WHEN IT POURS...

SYLLABLE **2** YOU USE ME TO PLAY A VIOLIN.

SYLLABLE **3** YOU DO THIS WHEN YOU EAT.

# THE NEXT HOST

The party is nearly over, so it is time to pick who will host the next Shopkins party! Cross out all the letters that are in pairs then work out the new host's name using the letters left over.

A
U J M E R J T L U
T M K A L K W D
R E W K U M B
B I L B

THE NEXT PARTY HOST IS...

?

___  ___  ___  ___  ___  ___  ___

# A PIECE OF CAKE

**It's Strawberry Kiss' birthday** and she is super-excited to see what her friends have planned. First, she goes to see Cheeky Chocolate.

**"Hey, Cheeky. What are you up to?"** asks Strawberry.

**"Errr…"** Cheeky quickly hides what she is doing behind her back. **"Nothing."**

**"Do you want to do something?"** asks Strawberry.

**"Errr… No, sorry I'm busy doing… nothing,"** pretends Cheeky.

Strawberry walks away sad that Cheeky has forgotten her birthday.

Next, Strawberry sees Apple Blossom looking for supplies.
**"Are you looking for some candles?"** asks Strawberry, hoping Apple has remembered her birthday.
**"No, why would I need candles? The lights are bright enough,"** replies Apple, with a little smile. Strawberry walks away, she can't believe that Apple has also forgotten her special day.

Strawberry then spots her friend Suzie Sundae chilling out.
**"Hi Suzie, do you know what day it is?"** asks Strawberry.
**"Errr… International shoelace day?"** replies Suzie.
Strawberry is upset that all her friends have forgotten her birthday and she storms off.

**"This is the worst, worst, worst birthday, ever!"** says Strawberry as she mopes around the Small Mart.

# "SURPRISE! HAPPY BIRTHDAY!"

cheer Cheeky, Apple and Suzie together. From behind their backs they show Strawberry their three fabulous birthday cakes they have been making! Then…
slip, slide and oopsy-daisy!
The three Shopkins fall over and their cakes fly high into the air… and land perfectly on top of each other, making the best birthday cake, ever!

Kooky Cookie skates over towards the birthday commotion. Kooky has iced the Small Mart floor to create a slippery ice-rink for Strawberry's birthday.
**"Happy birthday, Strawberry,"** says Kooky, as she gives Strawberry a pair of fab birthday ice-skates!

**"Thank you everyone, I knew you hadn't forgotten,"** says Strawberry. **"I love, love, love my birthday surprise!"**

# CHECK YA LATER!

# FAVOURITE DESTINATIONS

**The Shopkins are going on a world tour. Can you find out which famous city each Shopkins wants to visit?**

Decode the word wheels below by crossing out the first letter on each wheel, then every other letter to discover the answers!

**1**

**2**

**3**

# WORLD TOUR CREW

**Who's going to join the world tour? Lots of Shopkins have turned up wanting to go. Can you find which Shopkins don't have pairs in the muddled queue? They will be on the tour!**

# PASSPORT PATTERNS

The Shopkins are busy criss-crossing the world and they have collected lots of stamps in their passports. Can you complete the stamp patterns below? Only one of each stamp can be in each passport column and only one stamp of each location can be in each row.

*Let's meet in...* **PARIS**

# POSTCARD PAIRS

The Shopkins have taken lots of world-tour pics to use as postcards. Can you match the postcards pairs below?

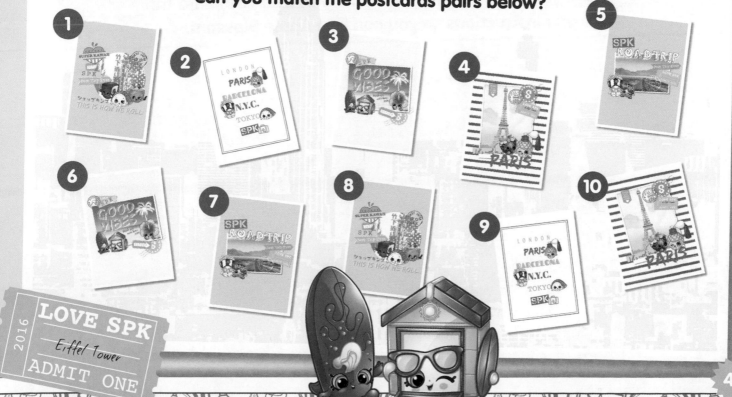

# WORLD TOUR MEMORY TEST!

There are lots of super-sweet moments for the Shopkins to remember on their big adventure. Have a look at these holiday postcards then cover the page and see if you can answer the questions on page 51.

# AROUND THE GLOBE QUIZ GRID

**Oh no! The Shopkins have lost Apple Blossom somewhere on the tour! Answer the questions below to complete the grid instructions so you can find Apple Blossom.**

**1** HOW MANY LETTERS ARE IN THE WORD "LONDON"?     MOVE RIGHT ☐ SPACES

**2** HOW MANY NEW YORK STAMPS CAN YOU COUNT ON THE PAGE?     MOVE DOWN ☐ SPACES

**3** HOW MANY HEARTS DOES LIPPY LIPS HAVE?     MOVE LEFT ☐ SPACES

**4** WHAT SHOPKINS SEASON IS TOASTY POP FROM?     MOVE DOWN ☐ SPACES

**5** HOW MANY VOWELS ARE IN TACO TERRIE'S NAME?     MOVE UP ☐ SPACES

ANSWERS ON **PAGE 61**

# WORLD TOUR MEMORY QUESTIONS

**How much do you remember about the Shopkins holiday snaps?**
**ANSWER THE QUESTIONS BELOW.**

WHY NOT TRY THIS MEMORY TEST WITH A FRIEND AND SEE WHO GETS THE MOST QUESTIONS RIGHT?

1. HOW MANY SHOPKINS ARE THERE IN ALL THREE POSTCARDS?

2. WHERE IS MELONIE PIPS SPENDING HER HOLIDAY?

3. HOW MANY SHOPKINS ARE WEARING SUNGLASSES?

4. HOW MANY SHOPKINS ARE VISITING MEXICO CITY?

5. WHAT COLOUR IS THE FRUITY SHOPKINS' POSTCARD?

6. WHO IS ON HOLIDAY WITH PINEAPPLE CRUSH?

**Follow the completed instructions on page 50**
**and help the Shopkins find Apple Blossom.**

START →

LOVE SPK
Empire State Building
ADMIT ONLY

NYC
#NEWYORKCHIC

# MEET SEASON 8

## UK HOLIDAY

### KINGSLEY CROWN

Regal and brave! He's only seen at important engagements and goes everywhere with a fanfare!

♥ s playing king of the castle.

### FREDDY FISH 'N' CHIPS

A helpful Shopkin who always chips in. He's very enthusiastic, and gets wrapped up in everything he does!

♥ s walking along the pier.

### BRITNEY BAG

Britney Bag is a very patriotic purse. She's always flying the flag of her country.

♥ s royal spotting.

### KAY CUPCAKE

A pretty little cupcake who's a high tea expert! Morning or afternoon tea – it doesn't matter! Tea time is any time for this proper Shopkin.

♥ s afternoon tea!

### HIGH TEA HELEN

A Shopkin who loves thrills and spills. Sometimes a bit hot headed but always keeps calm and carries on!

♥ s having high tea of course.

## ITALIAN TOUR

### MARIA MOPED

A Shopkin who loves life in the fast lane! Maria Moped zips around Italy, and she always goes faster after a bowl of fresh pasta!

♥ s watching motorcycle racing.

### BETTINA BAG

Bettina Bag handles everything with Italian style. Loves the night life and has a passion for fashion!

♥ s sightseeing and selfies.

### GINO GELATO

Cool, colorful and a cone full of fun. Strangely he loves having brain freezes.

♥ s cooling off in a piazza.

### CARLO COFFEE POT

A hot headed Italian whose rich and smooth dance moves always impress his friends. It's how he lets off steam!

♥ s staying up late at night.

# FRENCH ADVENTURE

## BABETTE BAGUETTE

A shy little Shopkin who doesn't like coming out of her bag.

♥s long lunches.

## ELLA TOWER CAKE

When it comes to sweetness, Ella towers above the rest. She's a true icon of French baking!

♥s sightseeing and eating.

## PETITE PERFUME

A small bottle who always makes scents. Sometimes she's a bit self scented!

♥s spraying herself around town.

## BRIDGETTE BAGDOT

A stunning little bag who always carries herself with style. Always ready to handle anything!

♥s watching French movies.

## FLUFFY SOUFFLE

The perfect French dessert who rises to the occasion. This little Chef is always upbeat and never flat!

♥s attending cooking classes.

# SPANISH STOPOVER

## CLAUDIA CAKE

Pretty as a rose and as sweet as a sugar, Claudia Cake is the perfect Shopkin to share dessert with.

♥s cake decorating herself.

## DANIELLA DRESS

A free flowing Shopkin who loves to take the stage. Every move she makes is full of grace.

♥s flamenco dancing.

# MEET SEASON 8

## HANS ACCORDIAN

This little accordion's life isn't full of ups and downs, it's full of ins and outs! But like they say, life wasn't meant to be squeezy!

♥ s listening to polka music.

## TOCKY CUCKOO CLOCK

A very punctual Shopkin who's always on time. Some say she's a bit of a bird brain, but really she has a mind that works like clockwork!

♥ s bird watching.

### LIMITED EDITION

## LIL' ITALIA

Lil' Italia is a little brain freeze that you would love to have!
She is a sweet shimmering cone living inside a dome!

♥ s dreaming about ice cream.

## UK CUTIE

UK Cutie loves to shimmer and sparkle. A precious little jewel.
She is rarely seen but when she is out it's worth celebrating!

♥ s attending royal performances.

## PETITE PARIS

Sweet, petite and shimmering, Petite Paris is worth the search!
It's time to start the chase after this French tasty treat!

♥ s eating at Parisian cafes.

## JESS JET

A fast high-flying Shopkin. Jess Jet has her head in the clouds but always knows where she is going!

♥ s sky writing love letters.

## LIL' GLOBE

A little Shopkin who is always in a spin! Very well travelled and can speak many languages, Lil' Globe has a world of knowledge.

♥ s stargazing.

## FRENCHY TOWER

Frenchy Tower is an icon of Paris. No matter what part of the city you are in, you can't miss her beaming smile.

♥ s reading romance novels.

## BRITISH BEN

Likes to speak his mind very loudly every hour and a real stickler for being on time!

♥ s playing "What's the time Mr. Wolf?"

## CARRIE CASE

Loves to pack a lot into her day and always on the go. Not afraid to go on long trips and loves riding on baggage carrousels!

♥ s flying first class.

## LENA TOWER

Lena Tower may look wobbly but she is always steady on her feet. This charming little Italian attracts tourists from around the world.

♥ s doing yoga.

# DAY-DREAM-TRIPPER

**Where would you go on a world tour?**
**Doodle some of the locations on the postcards below.**

# WORLD WORDSEARCH

ANSWERS ON PAGE 61

The Shopkins love meeting new friends all over the world!
Can you find all the postcard locations in the world wordsearch?

| C | I | T | A | L | Y | W | Z | S | R | A | O |
|---|---|---|---|---|---|---|---|---|---|---|---|
| L | A | A | B | P | A | R | I | S | J | S | T |
| A | R | L | A | U | S | T | R | A | L | I | A |
| M | P | W | I | T | X | O | R | F | B | L | F |
| W | D | T | L | F | J | T | A | W | W | U | C |
| M | E | X | I | C | O | C | I | T | Y | Z | F |
| T | O | K | Y | O | S | R | B | U | D | D | V |
| N | W | C | Q | K | K | T | N | W | Z | G | Z |
| L | U | S | I | R | O | I | I | I | M | I | Y |
| C | L | O | X | P | Z | H | U | C | A | W | U |
| L | O | N | D | O | N | V | A | S | J | N | T |
| C | N | N | E | W | Y | O | R | K | P | E | Q |

THE YELLOW LETTERS ARE AN ANAGRAM OF THE SHOPKINS' FINAL DESTINATION. CAN YOU WORK OUT WHERE IT IS?

CIAO! ROME

SPK POSTCARD ITALY

NEW YORK
CALIFORNIA
LONDON
TOKYO
PARIS
AUSTRALIA
ITALY
MEXICO CITY

# SHOPKINS HOLIDAY QUIZ

Do you want a relaxing holiday? What type of holiday do you prefer and who will be your perfect holiday companion? Answer the questions and follow the lines to find out!

## HOTEL RESORT

You love the simplicity of a hotel resort with a cool pool and waiter service. Your perfect vacation BFF would be the chilled and relaxed... **SUZI SUNDAE!**

**START HERE**
Is going on holiday all about relaxing?

NO →

**Does your adventurous side mean jungles and ancient ruins?**

YES

NO

YES ↓

**Are you a sunny seaside lover?**

NO

YES

**Do you relax by the pool?**

YES

NO

**Is your break away all about culture?**

YES

NO

## BEACH HOLIDAY

You love nothing more than to chill out and relax in the sun by the sea. Your perfect holiday bestie would be the fun and bouncy... **SPLASHY BEACH BALL!**

## CITY BREAK

For you, holidays are about experiencing local culture and some super-sightseeing. Your perfect city break mate would be... **HARRIET HANDBAG!**

## SKI TRIP!

Your holidays are full of fun and action! You love hitting the ski slopes by day and relaxing in the cabin at night. Your perfect cool-action partner would be... **POPSI COOL!**

## SAFARI TIME!

You love adventure and the exotic! You want to see nature but still relax in luxury. Every safari adventurer needs to be dressed like one, so your perfect travel mate is...
**HATTIE HAT.**

**YES**

**Is spotting exotic wildlife your idea of heaven?**

**NO**

**NO**

**Are holidays just quick pit-stops between everyday adventures?**

**NEW YORK, N.Y. SPK 15 2016**

**Do you plan trips to a timetable?**

## WORLD TOUR

You want to see the world and experience all it has to offer. You'll need somewhere to write all your special travel memories, so your world-tour bestie would be...
**SECRET SALLY.**

**YES**

**YES**

**NO**

## TRAIN TOUR!

You have all your tickets booked and your tour is ready to leave the platform! Your perfect train buddy with all the buffet-car know-how is... **MINI MUFFIN!**

**AUSTRALIA SPK POSTCARDS**

## BACKPACKER

You know which continent you want to visit and your backpack it packed. With a heavy backpack, you need some comfy footwear, so your perfect backpacking partner is... **SNEAKY WEDGE!**

## PAGE 8
**Bags Ready**

**Make-up Muddle**

## PAGE 9
**Who am I? Bertha Bath.**

Cosy Close-ups **1. Rolly Sleeping Bag,
2. Jessie Dressing Gown, 3. Bun Bun Slipper,
5. Anna Pajamas, 6. Sandy Shut Eye.**

**Close-up 4 is the odd one out.**

## PAGE 10
**Phone-a-Friend Puzzles**

**1. Poppy Corn, 2. Bubbles, 3. Heels.**
Slumber Shadows **1-e, 2-b, 3-a, 4-f, 5-d.**

**C: Strawberry Top has no shadow.**

## PAGE 11
**Photo 3 is the odd one out.**

## PAGE 18

## PAGE 21
**The secret dinner guest is Jessicake.**

## PAGE 29
Tidy Kitchen: **Fruit Shopkins: Cherry Anne,
Pippa Lemon, Buncho Bananas. Baking
Shopkins: Shelly Egg, Miss Sprinkles, Fleur
Flour. Utensils Shopkins: Judy Jug, Whitney
Whisk, Bessie Bowl.**
Missing Ingredient: **Choc Chips.**

## PAGE 30
**Tablecloth Travels**

**Main Course Clues Sammi Scrambles.**

## PAGE 34
**Invitation Misprint 3 Is the correct invitation.**

## PAGE 35

**Perfect Bunting** **e is the super-sweet bunting.**

**Guest List Search**

## PAGE 42

**Groovy Shadows** **1-g, 2-e, 3-f, 4-h, 5-a, 6-d, 7-b, 8-c.**

**Party Patterns** **Hot Choc - 9, Jiggly Jelly - 13, Mel T. Moment - 10.**

## PAGE 43

## PAGE 45

**Dance Queen** **RAINBOW BITE.**

**The Next Host** **MILK BUD.**

## PAGE 48

**Favourite Destinations** **1. PARIS, 2. TOKYO, 3. NEW YORK.**

**World Tour Crew**

## PAGE 49

**Passport Patterns**

**Postcard Pairs**

**1-8, 2-9, 3-6, 4-10, 5-7.**

## PAGE 50

**World Tour Memory Test**

**1. 8, 2. Venice Beach, 3. 2, 4. 3, 5. Pink, 6. Melonie Pips.**

**Around the Globe Quiz Grid**

## PAGE 57

| C | I | T | A | L | Y | W | Z | S | R | A | O |
|---|---|---|---|---|---|---|---|---|---|---|---|
| L | A | A | B | P | A | R | I | S | J | S | T |
| A | R | L | A | U | S | T | R | A | L | I | A |
| M | P | W | I | T | X | O | R | F | B | L | F |
| W | D | T | L | F | J | T | A | W | W | U | C |
| M | E | X | I | C | O | C | I | T | Y | Z | F |
| T | O | K | Y | O | S | R | B | U | D | D | V |
| N | W | C | Q | K | K | T | N | W | Z | G | Z |
| L | U | S | I | R | O | I | I | I | M | I | Y |
| C | L | O | X | P | Z | H | U | C | A | W | U |
| L | O | N | D | O | N | V | A | S | J | N | T |
| C | N | N | E | W | Y | O | R | K | P | E | Q |

**The Shopkins' final destination is SHOPVILLE.**